a story for all ages

change

judith barnes and erick james

illustrated by jeff grader

For Mary Cowan
To honor her commitment to growth, change, beauty and friendship.

Other books by the authors

Good to be Here by Judith Barnes
How Not To Suck at Communication by Judith Barnes and Erick James
How Not to Suck at Mentoring by Judith Barnes and Erick James

Copyright © 2010 by Judith Barnes and Erick James.
All rights reserved.

ISBN: 978-1-935534-61-7

Printed in the United States of America
by Classic Graphics, Charlotte, North Carolina

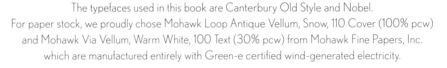

The illustrations for this book were created with black pencil, ink, gesso, and collage
with final preparation using Adobe® Illustrator® and Photoshop® on a Mac.

The typefaces used in this book are Canterbury Old Style and Nobel.
For paper stock, we proudly chose Mohawk Loop Antique Vellum, Snow, 110 Cover (100% pcw)
and Mohawk Via Vellum, Warm White, 100 Text (30% pcw) from Mohawk Fine Papers, Inc.
which are manufactured entirely with Green-e certified wind-generated electricity.

Book design by Michael Chrisner in creative collaboration with Judith Barnes.

Change is the first Word Book in the series The Story of Communication.™
"The Story of Communication" is a trademark of Judith Barnes.

"The universe is change; our life is what our thoughts make it."

— *Marcus Aurelius*, *Meditations, IV, 3*

To all who change themselves and the world for good.

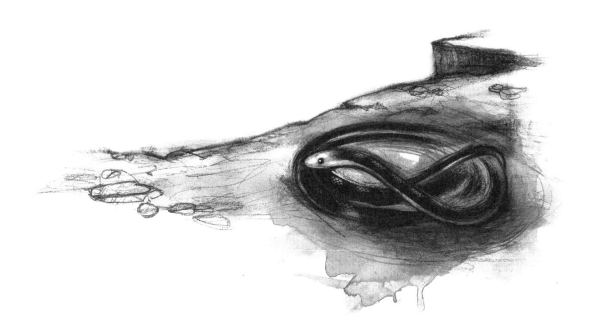

This is the story

of a young desert snake.

Her skin was a glistening bronze with gold and silver markings.

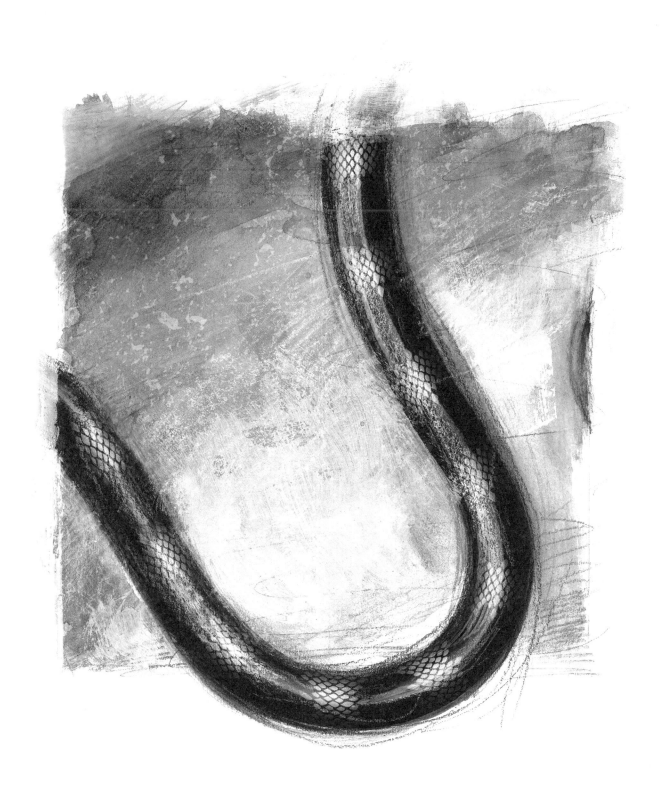

In sunlight, her skin
glowed warm and rich.

Under the full moon,
it shimmered with
an icy glint.

The snake was very beautiful.

But she was very scared.

"You will
often shed
your skin,"
older snakes
had told her.

She did not want to shed her beautiful skin.

She would not rub against rocks or sticks

to loosen her skin as she had been told to do.

She was determined not to change.

Trying desperately to keep her skin,

. . . and stay exactly as she was, she moved less and less.

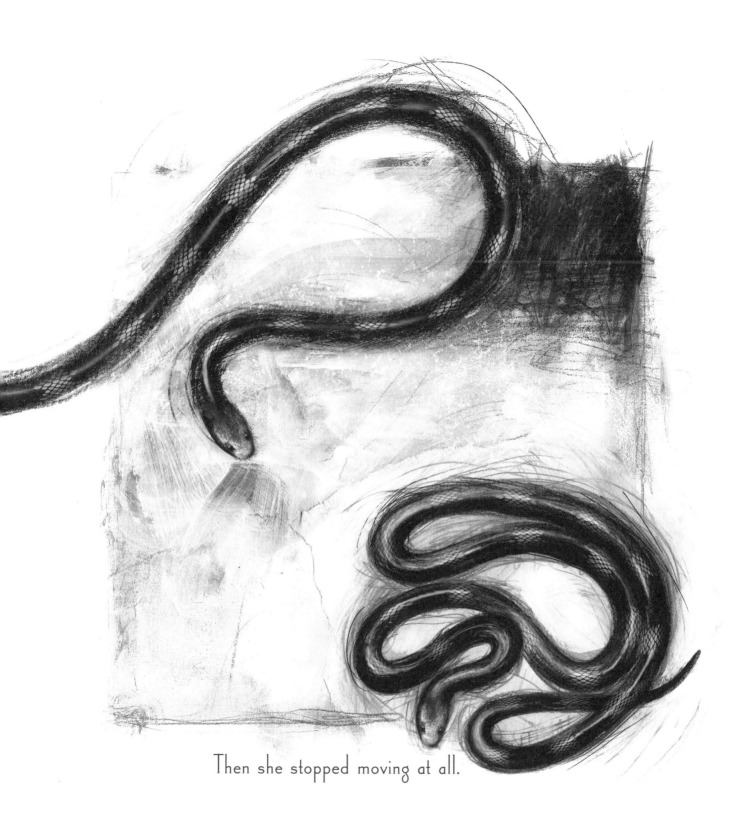

Then she stopped moving at all.

She lay coiled
at the edge
of the canyon.

The hot sun beat down on her   day   after   day.

But
she
would not
move to find
shade or water.

Small animals darted by but she would not move to eat.

Birds flew above, waiting for her to die so they could feast on her.
But she would not move to safety.

The nights were cold and dark and filled with other dangers.

But still she lay motionless.

One night . . .

a coyote slipped soundlessly

out of the black silence.

Day and night, he had watched her.

Now he circled, more curious than threatening.

"Why have you stayed here, Snake?" he hissed.

In a whisper so weak it almost
disappeared into the cold night air,
she told him of her fears.

His sudden, wild laughter

shattered the silence and seriousness.

"Look what you've done to yourself. . . .

The real danger comes from not changing, Snake.

Life is change. My advice? Accept it. Enjoy it."

Then he vanished into the shadows
as the sun began to rise.

The snake turned slowly, surprised at what she saw in the dim light.

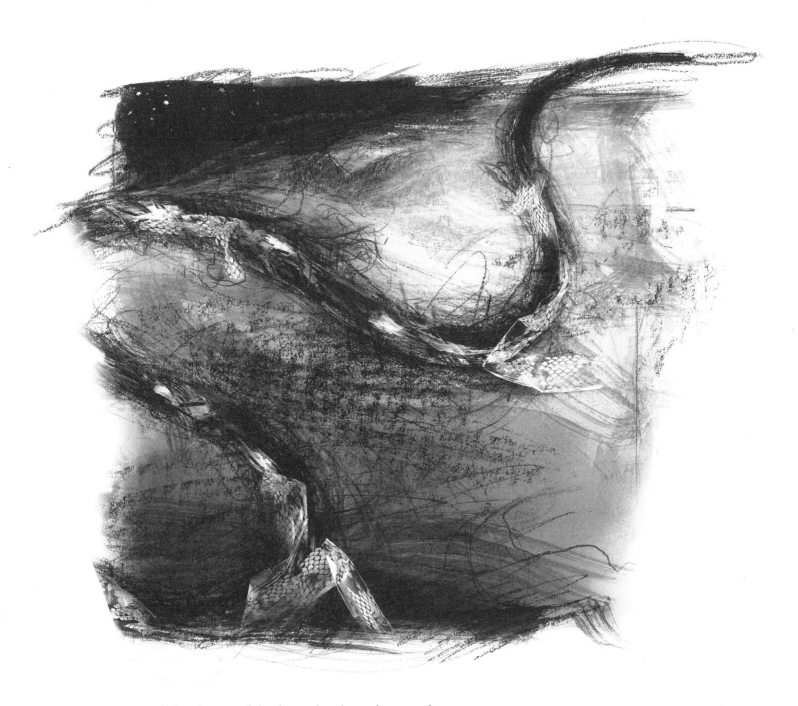

The beautiful skin she loved was dry.

C r a c k e d.
Colorless.

Dead.

But she was still alive.

And when she twisted around and looked closer,

she saw new skin underneath the old.

She slithered and slid wildly in relief,
sloughing off her old skin
in the cool breeze.

Finally, exhausted, she fell asleep at the edge of the canyon.

Then as the sun rose higher,

she rolled over and looked back at her beautiful new skin.

She was filled with joy.

Why had she made this so hard,

she wondered, as she looked over at her old skin . . .

. . . shed along with her fear of change.

The coyote is right.

Often the real danger comes not from making a change but from fighting it or fearing it.

There's nothing negative or frightening in the definition of the word change: it means to become or make something new and different, to arrive at a fresh phase.

But words also evoke feelings which means change can feel like a good thing or a bad thing—an opportunity or a threat—and that can make changing either easy or very difficult, as the snake learned.

Snakes regularly shed their skins. So do we.

We make many changes in a lifetime. So how we define change can shape who we become and how we live our lives.

The snake is not the only one who can benefit from the coyote's good advice.

Accept change. Enjoy change.

> "It is not because things are difficult that we do not dare,
> it is because we do not dare that they are difficult."
>
> — *Roman statesman and philosopher Lucius Annaeus Seneca* (ca. 4BC-65AD)

judith barnes, Ph.D.

Judith Barnes believes in the art, science and often magical benefits of communication. She is an educator, entrepreneur, speaker and writer with a four-decade consultancy in communication that has provided ample, amusing and often inspiring material for her books. Her essays have aired on public radio, and she was co-writer and executive producer for a short film on personal responsibility (www.thecruxmovie.com) screened at many festivals and featured on a public television program. Barnes has an M.S. and a Ph.D. in Communication from Rensselaer Polytechnic Institute. To see her work visit www.judithbarnes.com.

erick james

Erick James is a business development consultant working with companies to increase profitability through innovation and improved processes. He has a B.S. in Mechanical Engineering from Rensselaer Polytechnic Institute and a graduate Diploma in Management Studies from Cambridge University, UK. A true Coyote spirit, James is also a professional stand-up comedian who tours clubs and colleges nationwide, has had cartoon lines published in *Reader's Digest*, and performs as a magician for children and for adults with open minds. Visit www.erickjamescomedy.com.

jeff grader

Springing from the wilds of western Massachusetts, Jeff Grader finds artistic inspiration in the woods, progressive house music, zombies and the contrasts that surround us all. Grader holds a B.F.A. in illustration from Massachusetts College of Art. Since 1995, his visions have appeared in magazine articles, books, character designs, animations, Web sites and countless advertising and marketing materials. *Change* is his first picture book. Grader would like to thank his golden retriever Duke for his yeoman service and infinite patience as a model for Coyote. See his work at www.warpedwhimsy.com.

michael chrisner

Creative director Michael Chrisner is a graphic storyteller and book lover... a lover of paper, printing, typography, and image—merging ideas with form. Above all, Chrisner is a teacher and collector, sharing all that he has with those who embrace collaboration. He enjoys creating great beauty, meaning and results through creativity and by challenging the visual status quo. His B.F.A. from Parsons School of Design marked the beginning of a gordian professional journey that is chronicled at www.designsmallplanet.com.